MW00809811

MY STORY OF US: ZACH

Story of Us Series Book #1

CHRIS BRINKLEY

www.smartypantsromance.com

Copyright

Made in the United States of America

Print Edition
ISBN: 978-1-949202-62-5

May your world
Always be
Filled
with wonderful
Stories.

[illegible signature]

Part 1

JANUARY 1ST

I've never really written a diary or a journal before, but here we go. I am writing this for you. It's the first day of the new year and when I woke up this morning, I wondered what it would be like to wake up next to you. Cheesy, right? But it's true. We've only known each other for a few months, but somehow, I know. I know that when I see you, my day gets a little better. I know that when we talk, the minutes fly by. When we talked on the phone last week—when you were telling me about the work project you needed help with—I completely lost all concept of time. I was driving to my parents' house and now, looking back, I can't tell you anything about the drive. I don't know if the sun was shining, if it was raining, if I drove through a monsoon, if I drove fast or slow, or stopped at any red lights. The only thing that had my attention was you. You had to go because you had to get back to work, and when we hung up, I looked at my phone and it said we talked for fifty-three minutes and twenty-two seconds. Can you believe that? Fifty-three minutes and twenty-two seconds. I don't do anything for fifty-three minutes and twenty-two seconds—especially talk to someone on the phone. I have the attention span of a goldfish, and I hate being on the phone.

I don't even understand what you're doing to me. I'm a different person when I'm talking to you or thinking about you. You make me see a side of myself that I didn't know existed. Right now, I'm sitting at my table writing our story and I have named it, "My Story of Us." I feel like I'm back in high school and have a serious crush. There is a football game on right now, but I have the TV off and I am writing about you. What is happening to me?!

Here is what I don't know: I don't know what you think about me. I don't know if you think about me when we are not together, or if I make your day a little brighter. When we hung up the phone last week, you could have said to yourself, "That was the longest fifty-three minutes and twenty-two seconds of my life! That guy won't shut up." You may think my hair is too short or wish I had a beard. You may like older men or younger men or guys with tattoos, or even girls with tattoos. Who knows? All I really know is how I feel towards you, and I can't shake all the thoughts of you bouncing around in my head.

So, I am going to write this journal thing, this story, this "My Story of Us." And if there never is an "Us," then I'll throw it away. Nobody will ever know. I'll be a guy who had a crush on a girl, put it into words, and then felt ridiculous and got rid of it. But if you already have feelings for me, or one day grow to care for me the way I care about you, then our story is in words. Written words last a long time. And if we last a long time, we will always have my foolish notion called "My Story of Us."

So, it's January 1st and I like you. Everything about you. And soon, I am going to tell you, because I hope you like me too.

Happy New Year.

Part 2

JANUARY 4TH

When you called me this morning to talk about the project we're working on, the call was quick because you were at work and had a meeting soon. When we hung up, I already missed you. So, I sat down and wrote my list of new year's resolutions.

The first resolution is the most important one—at least, the one that I am most committed to. Before I tell you about them, I need to explain something. I read an article this morning that said about forty percent of the population sit down and make an actual list of goals and resolutions each year. Of that forty percent, over half quit following their plan in the month of January. The other half abandons ship by June. Sounds daunting, doesn't it? But a few make it. Apparently, there is a trick—well, a strategy, because trick isn't really a good word—that can increase your chance of success. The strategy is to tell someone. Tell someone what your goals are, and that alone will make you more accountable and more likely to stick with it.

So guess what? I'm going to tell you. You are my accountability person, right here in our Story of Us. I'm not sure if this is what the writer of the article really meant, but why not? I think you're the perfect candidate. The funny part is that if you ever read this, it'll be in the future, and you'll know I stuck to my resolutions. Especially the first one, because it's about you.

My first resolution is to win you over. To win your heart. Did I tell you I like you? A lot.

My second resolution is to be a better me. Because if I win you over, you deserve the best me I can be. And I think the best me I can be is a pretty good guy.

The second resolution—to be a better me—has a lot of subcategories. I won't bore you with the details, but I know where my strengths are and my weaknesses lie, and I know *how* to do what I need to do. I just need to actually do it. I want to do that for you. You deserve it, because you deserve the best in everything. Including me.

The third resolution is to turn down the volume. I'm not talking metaphorically here—I mean literally. Earbuds, television, radio. Look, my dad could be sitting on a cloud and not hear the thunder during a rainstorm. I want to be able to hear as I grow older. How could I enjoy our fifty-three-minute and twenty-two second phone conversations if I can't hear anything? The other day, an older guy at work told me he loved the new TV his wife had gotten him for Christmas. I asked, "What kind is it?" and he replied, "It's 12:15. Are you hungry too?" I don't want to be that guy.

So back to resolution number one: win your heart. I'm not exactly sure how to do that right now, but I'll figure it out. I will. Columbus figured out how to sail the ocean blue. Ben Franklin figured out electricity. I can do this. I know I can.

Part 3

JANUARY 7TH

We see thousands and thousands of people in our lifetimes. Most people are strangers, people we will never know. In cars, stores, in the spaces we live and move in. In pictures, on billboards, on television. Occasionally, if we are lucky, we see someone who pulls us in, sparks our interest. Our story would not be complete without me describing the impact you had on me the first time I saw you.

The summer right before I graduated from college, my grandmother asked me what I was going to do after I earned my degree. I hated that question because I didn't know. I'd changed majors three times but kept advancing the cause, going to class and making the grades. At the time, I couldn't see it. I couldn't visualize being out of school and in the real world as a true adult.

I answered my grandmother with the truth because I knew she wouldn't judge me. I told her I had no clue. Then, after an awkward silence, I took a shot at making her laugh by saying I'd probably take a nap after graduation, maybe order pizza. My dad would have said, "You better figure it out, son." Or, "You've been in school for four years and you still don't know?"

I braced myself for a similar response, but my grandmother sensed my uneasiness with the question. She smiled a little and said I had my entire life to figure it out. Then she said, "I normally don't give advice, but if I've learned anything in this life, it is this: follow your curiosity. Curiosity is an inner guide to purpose and passion. Explore what makes you wide-eyed and eager to learn more. Explore what keeps you up at night with unanswered questions. Pay attention to your curiosity. Let it be your guide."

I'll never forget her advice. "Let curiosity be your guide." Those words led me to my career and were as important as any words I ever heard in college. Those words are also why I'm writing this in my notebook right now. It's what I felt in the meeting the day my world brushed against yours. Curiosity.

I'd arrived at the meeting very early. I like to be prepared. I knew I would be making my presentation to three people, including you. You were the only person I hadn't yet met and I knew almost nothing about you beyond your name. I'd repeated it several times on the drive over because I always make it a point to call people by their names.

I had my back to the door when you walked into the room. I felt you before I saw you; I felt the energy in room change. I turned around, ready to welcome everyone, and you were the first person I saw. My balance shifted, both literally and figuratively. Something inside me wanted to reach out to you in that moment. Walk toward you, introduce myself only to you. I brushed off the instinct and looked away, collecting my thoughts for the meeting. I gathered my focus, said hello to the group, and formally introduced myself. I was suddenly nervous, which surprised me because I don't get nervous when I'm prepared. My voice sounded different in my own head when the words tumbled out of my mouth. I was prepared for the meeting, but I was not prepared for you. I was not prepared to look into your eyes and talk to you. Your presence shook me in the best way.

I made it through the meeting, but I wasn't really focused. I couldn't keep my thoughts centered. Admittedly, I am not a good multitasker, and I was completely distracted by you. When you spoke, I noticed everything. The way your eyes expressed your ideas. The way you rested your hands on the desk. Your timid smile. The way you looked away from me and then back at me when I was talking. It was a bit unsettling, but in a good way. I knew I liked it, but I didn't fully understand it. It had never happened to me before.

I now know what was happening that day. I was curious. About you. I wanted to know more. And not in some weird or creepy way. I just simply wanted to know more about you. Who were you? What books did you read? Who was your best friend? What kept you awake at night? What made you smile? What made you cry? What made you, you? And why were you having this effect on me?

My grandmother was correct. Pay attention to your curiosity. It is the inner guide to your purpose. And you, from the moment you walked into the room that day, made me a very curious person.

I wanted to know the answer to the question of you.

Part 4

JANUARY 12TH

Hey there! It's been a while. I haven't written in my notebook for over a week, but—and this is big—I have spent more time with you. I've seen you three times in the last week. We met once about the project, had a quick get-together at the coffee shop downtown, and we had lunch. I can't believe we ordered the same thing. You probably think I ordered what you ordered just to impress you, just to make you think we are a lot alike, but I didn't. That's what I always order when I eat there, down to the exact specifications. I thought, "I can't order that now, or she'll think I'm trying to impress her or imitate her, and that will creep her out," and for about a half-second, I talked myself into ordering something else. Then I just went with it and told the waiter I wanted the same thing. I'm not sure what you were really thinking, but you laughed and we talked about it. I think it's awesome that we like the same foods. If this all works out and we're still hanging out when we're old and can't eat as much, we can split meals. We'll save money—and calories.

I love our conversations. You say things that make me think, make me want to think. I hope you realize how very smart you are. When you were describing your hometown to me, I could see it. When you described the people in your life, I wanted to meet them. And I want you to meet my friends and family too. So, that got me thinking this morning.

There are some people you meet in life, and the more you get to know them, the more you like them. There is a guy I met last year when he joined the company and we began working together. His name is Kevin. His office is across from mine. He was nice, polite, and seemed like a good guy, but I still kept my distance because a lot of people have worked in that office and I assumed he would work there for a few months and then move on like the rest. At first, we would just say, "Good morning," or, "How's it going?" or whatever—the superficial chitchat that coworkers engage in every day. Then one day he asked me if I could look over his portfolio and give him some feedback because he respected my work and my opinion. So I did. And we talked and collaborated and became great friends. Now I trust his opinion and he trusts mine. Completely. Anytime I'm beginning a project, I lay out the groundwork, then get him to check it out. It just works. His insight helps me a great deal. He's like you—he's smart, and he makes me think. He helps me to see things and go in directions I would have never gone on my own. He makes my projects better.

And here's what I'm starting to think about you. You make "me" better. You make me see things differently. And just like Kevin makes me better at work—more creative and successful—you, my dear, make me better at being me. Collaborating with you in life would make life better. Ugh! The word "collaborate" is not a very romantic word, is it? I hope you get what I mean. I should probably stop while I'm ahead here. I'll sum this up by saying that I loved spending time with you this week. Every second. And I want to do it a lot more.

Part 5

JANUARY 27TH

Today was a big day. Circle this date in the official Story of Us. We kissed. I think that means you like me too. Scratch that! I *know* you like me too. You told me so.

Kissing. That's a big step. Since I'm the official historian of our story, or at least this diary, I will chronologically lay out the beautiful and stirring chain of events that led to this epic moment between us. I texted you. Suggested lunch. You texted back and said, "I don't think I can swing it. Crazy day." Then after I'd eaten lunch, you texted me again and said, "I have decided that the one thing I need the most on a crazy day is lunch with you." I'll be honest, I was flattered. I decided I'd meet you for lunch even though I had already eaten. I didn't tell you I'd eaten because then you wouldn't have wanted to go. But trust me, it was the right decision. I'm glad we went to lunch. I got to experience your sweet lips.

I got to the restaurant and sat there waiting for you for a long time. I watched an older gentleman to my left drink three cups of decaf coffee and read the business section of the newspaper. I listened to the lady at the table in front of me tell the person she was with that her daughter was moving back in with them and how this would either be a great decision or go horribly wrong because there is a fine line between being a supportive parent and being an enabler. (I agree with that.) And I watched a server handle money at one table and then refill a glass at another table while holding the glass around the rim where your mouth goes and—well, you know what a germaphobe I can be. Enough said.

So anyway, you got there, and you were so frazzled. I knew the moment I saw you that you were truly having a crazy day. Then it just got crazier. They messed up your order. You realized you left your phone in the car. There was a bratty kid in the back of the restaurant with his dad, who was definitely an enabler and will not only let the bratty kid move back in with him when the bratty kid is an adult but will also give him a new luxury car and full access to his bank account. They frazzled me too, and I was not the one having an already crazy day.

Then, as we were leaving the restaurant and walking to our cars, it began to rain—like, bottom-falling-out-of-the-sky, it's raining-cats-and-dogs-and-giraffes-and-elephants kind of rain. January rain is not fun. We got in your car because it was closer than mine, and you apologized because you had just helped a friend move and your car was crammed with boxes and papers and clothes and stuff. As we sat in your car and you continued to apologize about the scattered debris, I watched the rain drip from your hair and saw the chaotic mix of frustration and resignation in your eyes. I wanted to hold you, hug you, comfort you. But we were soaked, and car hugs never really work anyway. So I grabbed your hand mid-word of your fourteenth apology and said, "It's okay." Then I kissed you.

For historical purposes, our first kiss was quick and light and unexpected. It was unexpected even by me. I just reacted. I wanted to take away your crazy day. After the kiss, my brain caught up with my body, and I immediately realized I may have crossed a line and made a terrible mistake. But when I looked into your eyes, the chaos was gone. Your eyes told me that kissing you in that frazzled moment in your crazy day was the best thing I could have ever done. And then you said, “You’re right. It *is* okay. Please do that again.”

Again, for historical purposes, let it be known that our second kiss was anything but quick and light and unexpected. Our second kiss told me you’ve been thinking about me like I’ve been thinking about you. And I want a lot more kisses from your sweet lips. I should stop there because I don’t think either of us is ready for what the second kiss really told me.

But for historical purposes, that second kiss spoke loud and clear.

Part 6

FEBRUARY 1ST

You want to know something? I love you. I am falling deeper and deeper in love with you every second of every day. It's wonderful and it's scary and it's so far out of my comfort zone that I can't breathe when I stop and think about it. Today, when someone mentioned Valentine's Day, all I could think about was what I could do to let you know how much I love you. I want to do something for you that will show you how I truly feel. Something that will take your breath away and that you'll remember decades from now.

Because I love you. It is as simple as that.

Part 7

FEBRUARY 14TH, VALENTINE'S DAY

I never truly understood Valentine's Day before today. I just thought the holiday was created to sell candy and flowers and cards with words on them I'm not clever enough to come up with on my own. I even remember being in middle school seeing girls walking out of the building after school with balloons and flowers and them being so happy. I mean, I understood it, but I didn't really get it. If anything, I was kind of jealous. Not jealous of the happy girls, but jealous of the guys who knew how to make a girl feel that way. It seems ridiculous now, but I was only twelve or thirteen years old. How did guys that age even know how to call a florist and order flowers? Where did they get that kind of money? Or nerve? They were a lot more mature than I was. Girls and romantic stuff always felt like an elusive language I'd never understand, and Valentine's Day was a mystery written in that language.

Well, this year, I finally got it. I understood Valentine's Day. I haven't been able to stop thinking about how much I wanted to show you that I loved you. It's been on my mind ever since I told you I loved you and you looked at me with those sweet eyes of yours and told me you loved me too.

You know, there's something about holidays and us that might be beautifully connected. You were in my head on New Year's Eve. I started writing "My Story of Us" on New Year's Day. Now this. Our first Valentine's Day was . . . well, really, really, good. And If I am not mistaken, we had a pretty good Groundhog Day too! That's the day we spent all afternoon just hanging out inside and only went out long enough to see our shadows, then scurried back in again. (By the way, my shadow thinks your shadow is pretty hot.)

Speaking of hot . . . you looked fantastic tonight. I wanted to do something special for you, simply because I think you deserve it. And since it was our first Valentine's Day, it needed to be memorable.

I've told you a lot about my grandfather. About how he is my role model, the best man—the realest man—I've ever known. If you want to truly know me, you need to know him. When my grandfather met my grandmother, he was very young, about fifteen or sixteen, and had aspirations to be either a major league baseball player or a baker. Kind of funny, isn't it? He wanted to make spectacular diving catches in the outfield turning triples into outs, or make pastries and cakes, turning flour and sugar into something that makes everybody smile. So, when he met my grandmother and they started "going steady" as he called it, he made her a coconut cake as a surprise. He really went the distance with the cake. He bought a fresh coconut, figured out how to cut that thing open, and shredded it by hand. He put his heart and soul into a cake he was making for a girl he was truly smitten with. And even though the cake was not very good—too dry, not sweet enough, "kinda flat," my grandmother used to say—they ate the cake and fell in love.

I know the cake story because every year at Christmas he would make a coconut cake and the whole family would sit around the table telling that story. And you know what? After fifty-plus years, my grandfather could make a really good coconut cake with fresh coconut and a little bit of sweetened condensed milk drizzled on top. Even after my grandmother got sick and could barely sit at the table, she would always eat at least one bite, because it was more than just a cake.

So, I wanted to do something you'd never forget on our first Valentine's Day. Your flowers were waiting for you when you got to work. The balloons came right after lunch. Your blanket came by delivery moments before you got off work. It was wrapped up in a box with a note inside that said, "Bring this with you when I pick you up at six."

At six o'clock I picked you up, and we drove to the museum. You said, "The museum is closed," and I said, "Not for us." What you didn't know was that the museum is one of my clients, and I used my connections with them. When I told them about you and how I wanted to do something really special, they were all in. We prepared for a week. I would give anything to have a picture of the look on your face when you saw I had a key to the side door and knew where the lights were, or when you realized I knew how to work the computer system in the planetarium.

That, my dear, was our first Valentine's Day—alone in the planetarium of the museum, on your new blanket, having a picnic under the stars. I don't know how to make coconut cake, but I do know how to show you what you mean to me. And if you'll let me, I'll do that every day for a very long time.

Happy Valentine's Day.

Part 8

MARCH 21ST

It's been over a month since I've written anything. Things are great with us and getting better. Do you know what it's like when you wake up in the middle of the night and you can't go back to sleep? How your mind wanders and goes to all of those crazy places? The issues at work, how you need to get your car serviced? Why is there prune juice but no plum juice when we have grape juice and not raisin juice? And if a prune is a dried plum, then how can you get juice out of it? It's dried!

Yeah, that stuff. Your mind thinks of crazy things when you wake up in the middle of the night and are trying to go back to sleep. Most of the time those things don't really matter. Well, last night, when I woke up at 3:21, I decided I'd think about something meaningful. I'd think about something that would make me happy. So, I thought about you. I thought about us. I came up with a list of five things I like about us. Five ways that, together, we fit. Here it is:

Number 1: Our smiles. I love the way we make each other smile. I catch myself with this grin plastered on my face all the time when I'm with you. I often think I should quit smiling so much, but I can't help it. And maybe you smile a lot because I'm smiling, but whatever the reason, I adore your smile. And if I could spend every day making you smile, I would, because your smile lights up my world. Everything is brighter and better and feels clearer. Does that make sense? Probably not. But it's the truth. And I hope right now, this very second, that you're smiling. Because my world is a better place when you smile.

Number 2: The way we order the same food. This is crazy. This happens every time we go out to eat. Every time. What's up with that? Further proof we were meant to be.

Number 3: Okay, this one is cheesy. I like the way our hands fit together. And yes, I know I'm a guy. You might be surprised to know I remember the first time we held hands. We were walking and talking, and I reached over and just grabbed your hand. I wasn't even thinking. It wasn't planned, I just did it without even looking. And I remember thinking, "Wow, should I have done that?" And then thinking, "Holding her hand feels really easy. Natural." I liked how perfectly our hands fit together. How soft your hand was. How good it felt. When I reached over to hold your hand at the movies a few days later, I wasn't thinking about the movie. I wanted to test my memory. I wanted to see if our hands really did fit perfectly together. And my memory was spot-on. We're good hand holders. And when it comes to my hand and yours, just listen to that Beatles song.

Number 4: Our conversations. When we talk, the rest of the world fades away. I want to turn down the music and turn off the television and just concentrate on our conversation, on your voice. You are so smart. You see the world like I do, but differently. Do you know how many things I've already learned from you? That's why I like talking to you. Because my world grows. And if we really are confined to the limitations we create for ourselves, then you expand my world. You know what? It's kind of exciting to think about what the two of us could accomplish together. It's mind-blowing, really, but I'll move on to number five.

Number 5: Finally, I like us. I like me with you and you with me. This is my favorite thing. It's when everything else falls into place. And it doesn't matter when or where we are. Six a.m. or midnight, on the sidewalk or on the couch, alone or with people (although I do like our alone time). It doesn't matter. I like us. Me and you. Together.

Part 9

APRIL 11TH

Well, today we had our first disagreement. And you know what? This tells me we are real, because all I want to do right now is apologize and make it right. It hurts knowing that we are not in sync, knowing that our alignment is off-center and we're not connected like we always are. Like we're supposed to be.

I had a terrible day. It was one of the worst days I've had at work, ever. I've been working on a presentation for a client for almost a month now. It's a big deal for me and the company. If this proposal lands and we secure the client, it can lead to a long-term relationship that is beneficial for all of us. And it's one of the biggest projects and most influential clients I've been involved with. It's a potential career changer.

Throughout my whole life, whenever something truly matters, I get lost in it. I put my heart and soul into it. When I was a kid, I wrote a book. An entire book! I was ten or eleven and I decided I wanted to be a writer. So, I wrote every day. For my birthday, Mom had the book printed with a cool cover and my picture on the back. It was a real book! One hundred copies. Over 150 pages. I signed them all and gave copies to my family and my parents' friends. I even had a reading at the library. It made the front page of our local newspaper.

In college, I led a student committee to add more handicap parking areas because a friend of mine with cerebral palsy needed to arrive on campus almost an hour early so he could get to class on time. The issue was a lack of parking spaces. He had worked so hard to get a driver's license. He even had his car modified so he'd be able to commute to college. It was unfair that he'd worked so hard to overcome one obstacle after another and ultimately achieve his goal only to struggle again because there were not enough parking spaces on campus. He didn't complain, but I did. Because watching him walk to class in the rain, or worse, in a thunderstorm, was not an option. So I got involved with the student government association and we worked together to get the parking areas expanded. It took six months and a tenacity I didn't realize I had. Those parking spaces, I'm proud to say, are still there today. And guess what? My friend is now a professor at that university and will probably be a dean someday.

So, what I am saying is that when I get behind something and truly commit, I throw myself into it headfirst. That is what I'd done with this presentation for the client. It was good. No, it was great. We spent over 200 hours putting this together and it was fantastic. Then my boss walked in this morning and said, "We are going in a different direction." I'm all about adaptability and teamwork. But really? "Why?" I asked. Our presentation was a game changer. He hadn't even seen it yet, and I knew if he saw it, he would want to stay the course. But the bossman was dismissive. He didn't even let me explain. I'd never seen him like that before and I know whatever it is that had him changing direction is much bigger than I am. I get that. But 200 plus hours of my team's hard work will never see the light of day. That hurts. I know I'm getting paid to do my job, and this is my job, but it's about more than money to me. We put everything we had into that project.

So, I had a really bad day. And I forgot I was supposed to go with you tonight to that important dinner. I had too much on my mind and I just forgot. I was feeling sorry for myself and mad and confused. And you were already running late and stressed before I didn't show to pick you up. You snapped at me and I snapped at you and we had our first disagreement. I let you down. I forgot. And yes, as you said, I could have met you there. But trust me, you didn't want me there. I was not in the mood to be around people. As pleasant as I am most of the time, and as happy as I always am when I'm around you, tonight I just needed to be alone.

So, as I write this, I don't know. Here I am alone, writing about us. I'm worried. I've never made you mad at me. Or frustrated, or whatever it is you're feeling. I've never let you down before. I fear this may be the end, which would be terrible. I'm sorry. I'm truly sorry. I let work interfere with us. I'm going to bed and am going to wake up tomorrow in a better mood and apologize to you. Hopefully, we can work this out. Because you are more important than any project could ever be.

Part 10

APRIL 12TH

I guess I should call this entry "Our First Disagreement: Part 2" or "Resolution: The Sequel to the Disagreement." I slept last night and, like I had hoped, woke up in a better mood about the terrible day I had. Yesterday I was just feeling sorry for myself. I'm over that, which is what I'd hoped for. But just because I'd woken in a better mood about work, my mood about us hadn't been any better. I mean, I felt positive we could work it out, but I wanted to work it out as soon as possible. I wanted to make it right. So, I called you and apologized. I apologized for forgetting your dinner and snapping at you. You accepted and apologized for snapping at me too. And we decided to meet at the park for lunch. The sun was shining and the weather was perfect. Honestly, we needed a nice day.

We met, and we talked. And we talked. And we talked. And it was easy. I hope we can always work things out like this. Talk it out. Listen. Understand. It seems so basic. To just communicate.

When I was in college, I took several communications classes: Public Speaking, Comm 100, and a class called Interpersonal Dynamics. The Interpersonal Dynamics professor said that some people make fun of her class. They call it the "touchy-feely" class. She was constantly doing things to challenge our way of thinking and showing us how the way we communicate with others is layered. It's layered by our attitude, our body language, our willingness to be real. It's also influenced by the setting, past experiences, expectations, and a million other things we carry with us everywhere we go. I learned a very valuable lesson in that class—to listen. I learned how to really listen to what someone is saying. And during conflict, to listen even closer. Look the person in the eyes, let my guard down, and listen.

Today we listened to each other. And talked. And walked away from the park on this beautiful spring day closer to each other. We're closer now than we were the time we spent the whole day watching TV and cooking and taking naps. We talked through the whole experience and our future together. Through the process, we came up with two things: an understanding and a system.

First, the understanding. Two people in a bad mood at the same time is not a good combination. Last night, you were having your issues, and I was having mine. Even though our primary issues weren't caused by either of us, we took our frustration out on each other. And that caused a whole new issue with us. So, when one of us is in a bad mood and the other isn't, we'll lean on each other. I'll be your crutch and you'll be my cane. But if we are both in a bad mood, we'll say it. Throw it right out there in the open. And we won't bicker or argue and be petty. We'll wait until one of us is over our bad mood and is ready and able to be leaned on. As much as I love this little idea (and am actually really interested to see how it works with us) I don't think we'll be using it very often. We're too level-headed as a pair to both be in a bad mood at the same time. But just in case, we now have an understanding of the "We Are Both in a Bad Mood" rule.

And second, the system. I have a friend who practices the system with his wife, and they seem pretty happy. They've been married five years, have two kids, and their relationship works. At first, I didn't understand what in the world they were doing. Sometimes they would just randomly throw numbers out at each other. She would say, "Seven," and he would say, "Okay, let's do that." Or she would say, "It's a zero, just make a decision." And he would decide. With all these numbers flying around, it was like they were speaking in some kind of coded language or trading stocks on the stock exchange. It was weird.

Finally, I just asked him about it. He explained that when they're making decisions, they just cut to the chase and assign a numerical value to the desired outcome. He gave an example from the previous weekend where they'd planned to go out for dinner but couldn't agree on where to eat. She wanted Italian and gave it a six on a one-to-ten scale. He wanted Mexican because it was closer and he'd been hungry and wanted the chips and salsa the restaurant offered the moment they sat, but eating Mexican had only been about a three for him. So he ate a small snack and they went to the Italian restaurant because eating Italian was a six to her.

They did this with a lot of things in their relationship—how they parented their kids, where they vacationed, with intimacy. It's a fantastic way to cut through all the passive-aggressive mind games that plague so many relationships. It gets to the core. It also causes you to self-evaluate your own decisions and your choices and give them a value, which people forget to do. The key is—and this is vital—you have to be honest. You have to be honest with yourself and with your partner. If it's a one, it should be a one. And a ten should really be a ten.

I told you as we sat on the bench and figured all of this out that making our relationship work and getting past this was a ten for me. You said, "Me too." And we got past it and grew closer in our relationship. Because you're a ten, and anything that's a ten for you will be a ten for me too.

Part 11

MAY 25TH

I love music and the sound of the ocean as the waves crash along the shore. I love the brief silence you hear when you're driving in the rain and you go under a bridge; it gets me every time. And I love the sound of popcorn popping in a microwave and the *woosh!* a basketball makes when it goes through a net on a long shot that perfectly finds the cylinder. But the sound I love the most right now, my new favorite sound, is you when you laugh. Not your fake laugh or your that's-sort-of-funny, half-hearted laugh. I love your genuine I-couldn't-stop-this-if-I-tried-my-hardest laugh. That laugh is perfection. And today, I heard that sound a lot. It was at my expense, but it was worth it.

We were spending the entire day together. Going to the museum, eating at a place neither of us had ever been to before, maybe a movie if we were in the mood. It was just us and a day where we did stuff together.

So, this morning I woke up and eagerly anticipated our day. I'm going to admit something to you now that you might not be fully aware of. I try to look my best when I know I'm going to spend time with you. It's not that I don't care otherwise, but it matters a little more when I know I'll be seeing you. I normally polish my shoes and iron my shirt—or at least throw it in the dryer with that wrinkle-release stuff. And yes, I even have one of those man-groomer trimmer thingies with all the attachments. (Let me explain. There's a guy at work, and he couldn't care less, or has no idea, or doesn't have friends who are honest enough to tell him that he has hairs coming out of weird places on his head. I'm not comfortable enough to tell him, even though I do notice. And, weirdly, it makes me self-conscious, so I have a man-groomer trimmer thingy. And it's actually pretty neat.)

After my shower this morning, I was shaving when I noticed for the tenth time this week that I had a single eyebrow hair that was not at all on the same page with my other eyebrow hairs. In a rush, and on a whim, I thought I'd take care of that little eyebrow hair. So, I grabbed the trimmer thingy and got close enough to my eyebrow to get the one hair that refused to cooperate. But I missed. Well, actually, I didn't miss. I got the one little hair and, oh, about seventy-two of its closest friends. It was like cracking a peanut shell with a sledgehammer—complete and unnecessary overkill. And the really bad part is it was the middle half of my eyebrow. The outer edges were still perfectly intact. It's truly one of the dumbest things I've ever done. I looked like a cartoon character. Some of the things that ran through my head as I stared at myself in the mirror were: What would you think? Would an oversized pair of sunglasses cover it up? Could I put a bandage over it and pretend I had had a medical procedure? How long does it take eyebrows to grow back? If I did the same thing to the other eyebrow, would it make it look natural? Could I just completely shave them off? Did Mona Lisa have a brother?

When the doorbell rang and I answered the door, I had my hand completely over my eye and eyebrow. Of course, you were worried I had injured my eye, so I just blurted it out and told you what I'd done. "I accidentally shaved half of my eyebrow off!" I never thought that sentence would ever come out of my mouth. Your reaction was priceless. You were concerned, and inquisitive, and slightly amused. Then when I finally removed my hand from my eyebrow, you immediately looked away, looked back, then laughed as hard and genuinely as I have ever heard you laugh. And I laughed too. You looked away once more to compose yourself. Then you looked at me again and tried to stifle a laugh that would not to be denied. And I laughed again too. When I asked you if anyone would notice, you laughed more. And so did I. We laughed until we both cried. And then we laughed some more.

Instead of starting our day at the museum, we were at the makeup section of the department store. I had a bandage on my poor, pitiful, sad, incomplete, fractured eyebrow (as you called it every time you looked at it). We got back to my place with a handful of eyebrow pencils and this stuff that, well, I still don't understand. For the next thirty minutes, you were Michelangelo, and I was your Sistine Chapel.

Unlike Michelangelo though, no one will ever know about your masterpiece, because we made a pinky promise that you would never tell—at least not for three years. As you covered my mistake, you came up with a new cosmetic term: the eyebrow comb-over. That made us laugh again. And I know understand how difficult it is to work on someone's eyebrow when they are laughing that hard.

I lost part of an eyebrow today, true. But three wonderful things came from it. One, you were very close to me when you were executing the "eyebrow comb-over." I could feel you breathing, and that was hot. Two, we discovered your inner artist. What you did was magic. The bad eyebrow looks better than the good eyebrow. How did you do that? Three, you'll have to do this every day until it grows back so that I won't look like a cartoon character. We will be seeing a lot of each other, and you'll be all up in my space when you work your magic. Wait! There's a fourth. And four, today I got to hear you laugh. A lot.

Part 12

JUNE 3RD

Whoops. Someone read this before you did. My Story of Us—meant for our eyes only—has been read by someone else. It wasn't supposed to happen this way. But I'm alive and safe and here to tell the story, so I guess it's okay. My life wasn't really in danger. But it kind of felt that way.

I'm writing this now, the morning after one of the craziest days I've ever experienced, from the back porch of a 5,000 square-foot colonial home built over 100 years ago. It's both modern and old. The bathroom connected to my room has a flat screen television on the wall above a claw-footed bathtub. All the floors creak when you walk through the house, yet there are speakers built into the ceiling of every room connected to a sound system. This house confuses me, but in a great way.

As you know, I'm away this weekend, hanging out with five of my friends from high school. We get together somewhere in Tennessee during the first weekend of June every year. We play golf and Risk and whiffle ball and grill and just hang out. Basically, we are six grown men who get to act like our twelve-year-old selves for an entire weekend. We call it "Infinite Adolescence." Cool name, right? I'll take credit for the title of our yearly weekend. I came up with the name during an all-night game of nerf basketball the first year we got together. The six of us are scattered all over the country now, so it's nice to reconnect and spend time with friends who knew you before you were really you. We have a bond. It works. Fantastically.

The idea started two years after we had graduated from high school. Nathan, now a chiropractor, has always been crazy-smart and went away to school. He loved it, but missed hanging out with his friends. Even at twenty years old, he expressed it perfectly, explaining to us that every day at the academically lauded, private university he was attending, he had to be this intelligent and studious person. He hung out with other intelligent people who were equally bright and driven and put a lot of pressure on himself to belong and fit in. He IS intelligent and studious, but sometimes he wanted to stop trying so hard and just be who he'd always been with the guys who'd always been his friends.

He suggested an extended weekend every year where we could hang out and be ourselves. But here is the fun part: we couldn't be ourselves now. No, we had to be our twelve-year-old selves, those wide-eyed, pressure-free young men who played and laughed and made fun of each other in the silliest and most adolescent ways. So that is what we do. No alcohol, no shenanigans, but a lot of pizza and video games and laughs. We even have an "Old" jar, and if any of us begins acting too old and serious, someone will shout "Old" and the guilty party has to put a dollar into the jar. As soon as the jar hits twenty-five bucks, we order pizza. It's awesome. Someday, I hope you get to meet the Infinite Adolescence crew. You'll like them, and they'll adore you.

Anyway, we've done this long enough that we already have a routine. I always room with Thomas. He's a basketball coach at a small junior college. Yesterday, after dinner, five of the six us decided to play laser tag with these cheap toys Thomas had bought online. It was raining outside, so we decided to chase each other around the house inside. It became an epic game of hide-and-seek for grown men with cheap, laser-tag guns. After our third game, Thomas and I came up with a plan to hide somewhere in the house and shoot each other with our lasers. Thomas, ever the strategizing coach, realized that if you get shot, you lose five points. But if you shoot someone, you get ten points. We would hide somewhere and shoot each other, gaining five points each time, while the other knuckleheads ran around the house looking for each other. Brilliant, right?

We immediately went to the basement of the house and struggled to contain our laughter as our maniacal-yet-genius plan began to unfold. We stood there in the basement in our socks, racking up points as we blasted each other with plastic laser-tag guns. If my 12-year-old self could have seen my future-self, we would have high-fived each other.

Knowing we had beat the system and were going to win the game, we quickly grew bored and started fiddling with a locked door in the corner of the basement that had a fancy digital keypad on it. Somehow, Thomas figured out the code, and the door opened. We'd found ourselves a wine cellar! It was a room about four feet by eight feet, with mahogany wood, hundreds of bottles of wine, and an elaborate cooling system set at fifty-two degrees. I knew immediately we weren't supposed to be in there but realized simultaneously it was the best hiding place the world had ever seen. We would not only win laser tag with more points than everyone else, but we would also show our superior hide-and-seek skills by hiding in the room within the room that the others didn't even know existed.

We propped the door slightly open, patiently and eagerly waiting for the others to find us. One by one, the other three guys literally jumped out of their skin when we popped out from behind the door of our secret room screaming and shooting lasers at them. You should have seen the looks on their faces when they found us. It was fear and surprise, mixed with awe and a hint of jealousy because we had found this secret room first and not them. (Thomas and I decided we shall forevermore be known as Lewis and Clark when talking about that night.) I laughed until my side hurt.

Then the fiasco began.

With five of us in the wine cellar, the propped door somehow closed shut. I was the first to try and open it because it was a lot of people in a little room that was not designed for a lot of people. Imagine being on a crowded elevator at maximum capacity when two more people enter —with luggage. Yeah, it was really crowded. And the door wouldn't open, not even slightly budge. The very expensive keypad lock on the thick mahogany door had malfunctioned and locked five guys in a four-by-eight-foot room that was fifty-two degrees.

I will spare you the details, but it might have been the longest night of my life. We were in there until this morning, more than twelve hours later. Nathan, the chiropractor, found us. He had gone to bed early last night and slept through the fiasco thanks to an allergic reaction to pepper, two Benadryl, and the most comfortable bed in the house. When he woke up, we were nowhere to be found. Our cell phones, half-eaten snacks, and shoes were scattered throughout the house. He thought we'd been abducted by aliens. (I kind of wish he'd been right. Aliens would have been a cooler story, and a UFO probably would have been much more spacious.) When he found the five of us this morning, we were a little tipsy, slightly dehydrated, and we had bonded in an even stronger way because of the remarkable wine cooler experience. We remained stuck in the room for two more hours because the high-tech lock had truly malfunctioned. Nathan ultimately called the owners of the home, who are vacationing in France, and they unlocked the keypad with an app from their phone from Paris. *Muy bien!* Wait, that's Spanish. *Trés bien!*

I am telling you all of this because at about 3:30 am, our conversation in the wine cellar turned to you, us, and "My Story of Us." Thomas, my roommate, had found the notebook earlier in the day in our room and had read it. All of this spilled out after a couple of bottles of wine.

(Don't judge. We got thirsty.) At first the guys made fun of me. Because of that, I was mad at Thomas, who not only read it, but told the other three, in precise detail, about our story.

As you've probably figured out by now, I'm guarded when it comes to my personal life. I don't let many people in. The walls around me are pretty solid; so solid it might take an app and a person from another country to unlock the doors to some of my walls. But I realized I'm also guarded with you. Something holds me back when it comes to telling you how I really feel. It's the reason I'm writing this. It's safe, because you may never see it. That's not fair to you though, and I'm beginning to realize that. I should tell you how I really feel. You deserve that. Because you are wonderful.

As my childhood friends and I talked for hours in that tiny wine cellar (and drank a little more Merlot) I let my guard down. I told them all about you. About the moment I first saw you and how the room shifted. About your artistry with my eyebrow combover. About how you make me feel. Comfortable and anxious at the same time. Eager and scared. Eager to get to know you, all of you. And eager for you to pull back the layers of me. Yet scared. Very scared that I won't be enough for you. Scared that you like me now, but when you see the rest of me—the grumpiness when I'm hungry or sleepy, the way I fall asleep during movies, the grown man who still watches The Flintstones —you won't like me as much. Why I am telling you all of this? I think I'm still a little tipsy from the wine and lack of sleep. I need a nap.

I'll wrap this up by saying that as I began defending this notebook with our story in it to a group of men acting like twelve-year-old boys, I became passionate about telling them about you. I talked about you for over an hour. Thomas said he knew you were the one for me. The spend-the-rest-of-your-life-with-her one. He knew it by the way I wrote about you and described you. I'm glad I shared our story with them. I'm glad I defended this diary. I might be a little bit like this house. I'm a walking contradiction of old and new. The old me is guarded and struggles to share and process the way I really feel about you. So, I write it on paper because it is safer that way. Maybe the new me will be better at that. Maybe the new me can tell you in the moment how you make me feel. How you make me better. How I'll do anything for you. Maybe the new me will take those walls and shatter them into a thousand pieces. All because of you.

Part 13

JUNE 17TH

Recently I was flipping through television channels and came across a documentary about animals and their sense of smell. Elephants, bears, dogs, even sharks, all have an incredible sense of smell. These animals navigate a world that we don't even know exists. Some animals can smell the past, the present, and the future. The past is what was once there—maybe just a few years ago, maybe decades. They smell the present, the very moment they are experiencing; it's their key to survival. And they can smell the future in the wind, in the atmosphere. This is how animals sense storms in order to seek shelter. It's how they find prey. It's a complex world that goes way beyond the human experience. The documentary explained that when a dog smells pizza, the dog doesn't just smell pizza. The dog smells each individual characteristic of pizza, each element broken down into a singular fragrance—flour, tomatoes, cheese, basil, olives, meat.

What does this have to do with us? Well, tonight I landed tickets to the symphony. My friend couldn't go and gave us his tickets, so we went. And, unexpectedly, I experienced something I've never felt before. I heard music like an animal smells food. I heard the elements, together and separate. It's hard to explain perceiving music (something I've always known) on a much different level.

The concert was a symphony tribute to the movies. You looked great, by the way. And honestly, midway through, my mind kind of drifted. Even though we were at the symphony, I was chasing other thoughts that had absolutely nothing to do with the concert. Then you reached over and held my hand. You brought me back and made me realize I wasn't focused, wasn't in the moment. It's important to me that when I'm with you, I'm always in the moment. Experiencing our experiences with you, together.

So, I got my mind right, and I paid attention. The song was the *Harry Potter* theme and seeing it as I listened changed the way I heard it. I started to really focus, to absorb it. When I watched the violinists, the violins were slightly louder than the other instruments, magnified, crisp and clean in my ears. The same with the flute and the cello and harp. All the music was still there, but it was different. I watched and I listened, seeing and hearing music, holding your hand while we experienced together and individually each part of the whole.

Processing this later, I realized I had focused my five senses on the moment, and it was spectacular. I heard the symphony, and I watched the musicians with their instruments create the sound. Taste? Well, this might sound odd, but the mint in my mouth was part of the experience. Smell? I could smell you leaning against me, and—I've told you this a thousand times—I really like the way you smell. Touch? Your hand in mine, our fingers intertwined so naturally, is what carried me to the moment. When you reached over and held my hand, I felt you, and I felt your love.

I'm telling you about my concert sensory experience because I always want to experience the world like this. Aware. And especially with you. I always want to use my five senses and experience you on a much deeper level—pay attention to you, always be aware of you. See you, hear you, smell you, taste you, feel you. Always.

Part 14

JUNE 30TH

Thank you. Thank for being you and being so good to me. It has been a rough couple of days. Do you remember our conversation about being able to lean on each other when the other needs someone to lean on? Well, you've been a mountain for me. I know that it probably feels like I've pushed you away and haven't wanted you around, but I've needed you more than you will ever know. The moments with you have been my sanity, my peace. Thank you for being strong and sweet. For being you.

The call came at midnight. Woke me up from a hard sleep. At first, I thought it might be you, that you needed something. Then, when I didn't recognize the phone number, I thought about not answering. I only answered because I thought maybe you were on someone else's phone. Maybe something had happened. I couldn't not answer.

It was the hospital in my hometown. Dad had a stroke. They found him alone in his yard. No one knew how long he'd been lying there. My number was in his wallet. He was unconscious.

The first thing I thought of when I got the call was that it was pathetic that he'd been found alone in his yard. Like he was too inadequate to have a stroke around people, or at least in the damn house. I feel guilty about having that thought. Ashamed. But it's complicated. My dad is complicated. Our relationship is complicated.

I've tried to explain it all to you while also sparing you the details. My scars. His scars. I'm not one of those people who puts it all out there for everyone to see. And because of that, it's hard to know when it's okay to show someone who we truly are. It's not that I don't trust you; I trust you more than anyone. It's just that I simply don't know how. I don't know how to truly let my guard down and let you see the scars I have somehow successfully hidden from the rest of the world—and from myself. I don't want to see them. Why would I want to show them to you?

I'll try to explain on paper what I can't seem to say to you in person. I'm taking off work for a few days and going to see him. I know he needs me. And as much as I know that you want to go with me and be supportive, I'm not ready for that. Please trust me when I say it has nothing to do with you. I don't know what I'll find. His life has been an unpredictable roller coaster. This is just another part of the ride.

I'll start with this: he's an alcoholic. He'll tell you he's an alcoholic. He's been to AA and rehab and therapy and done all the things you do to fix an alcoholic. But he can't be fixed. And I love him. I still love him. I have tried to fix him, but he can't be fixed. I feel sorry for him, but I'm angry and frustrated. I feel responsibility and the need to flee. I feel both love and hate and a thousand other emotions that don't belong together in the same box. He loves me too, but sometimes I wish he didn't because that's why it hurts so damn much. He crawls into the bottle and lives there in his own little world, getting himself into the messes that the rest of us try to clean up. Rinse and repeat.

Yet he's a really good man with one terrible weakness that he can't seem to shake. So many people who once tried to fix him have just moved on, gone on with their lives and quit wasting their energy on him and his disease. Mom moved on. His second wife moved on, and so did his third. His brothers moved on. But I haven't. Because he's my father. And I still love him. And even though I've completely let go of fixing him, I can't let go of *him*. So, I'll go back to my hometown and try to figure all of this out. See what is left of him and if he has anyone left in his corner.

Your desire to jump in and help me has made me love you even more. But for your sake and mine too, I'm not going to do that to you. This is our mess, not yours. No—this is *his* mess, not mine. But sometimes you need to step up and do things that have to be done because it's the right thing to do. Hopefully, I'll figure this all out and be back home to you next week.

Again, thank you for being you. Even though I don't do a very good job showing you how much I need you, I do.

Part 15

JULY 4TH

We were supposed to go to the big Fourth of July show tonight. But I'm here, and you are there. And I miss you. Terribly. I miss looking at you and listening to you. Most of all, just being with you. I miss knowing you're with me, in the same space, breathing the same air.

Being back here brings back so many memories of Dad. I vividly remember going to my first major league baseball game. Dad surprised me with the tickets for my birthday, and we went, just the two of us. Two guys going to a game together. I remember every detail. We were standing outside of the stadium getting ready to go through the ticket turnstiles along with all the other people waiting in line to go inside and see the game. It is one of the first times I remember getting caught up in something I thought was much bigger than I was. Thousands of people were excited and ready to experience something together, in the same space, at the same time. I was really young and for the first time, I realized the world was a big place, and I was just a small part of it. I also realized that every time there was a baseball game here in the stadium, this happened. My dad watched most of the games on TV, and if I wandered into the room, I would watch part of the game with him.

It was so much different actually being at the stadium, immersed in the crowd.

Dad and I had a great time that day. He bought me a baseball and one of those miniature bats. As we watched the game and screamed and yelled for our team, I felt so much older than my actual age. He seemed so much younger. I asked him if we could meet the players after the game and maybe get everyone on the team to autograph my baseball. He said we probably couldn't do that. But he told me to think about this—that those professional baseball players who were the best in the world, that we watched on TV, were here in this stadium with me. They were breathing the same air as I was. The air went into my lungs and then went out. And my air went into their lungs while they were on the field playing baseball. They breathed it in before they hit the ball, and caught the ball, and went into the dugout. "Your air," he said. "They are breathing your air. That is better than any autograph." To this day, I don't know why he told me that. I don't know if it's something he made up on the spot or had thought about a lot. But that's what he told me, and after he said it, I breathed in a little deeper. And I've never forgotten it. Sometimes now, when I am in a crowd or on an airplane, I think about that. How we are all breathing the same air. All of mankind.

When I first came back to my hometown and spent the first two nights in the hospital with him, it made me feel closer to Dad. Breathing his air. He still hasn't spoken, but he has squeezed my hand. I know he knows I'm here. I know I'm where I'm supposed to be. But I still miss you. Damn, I miss you! I don't know if you've ever spent the night in a hospital, but sleep is hard to find with all the beeps and buzzes, nurses and doctors, and traffic in the hallway. So I lie here awake, missing you.

When we talked today, it made me miss you even more. You are my escape. I'm on edge, and I'm so angry. But when I heard your voice today, the anger lifted, and I felt the calm I needed to make it through this day. You made me laugh when you told me about that funny thing that happened to you, and you made me smile when you told me you missed me, and you me made me think about the world a little differently, which you always seem to do when I talk to you. For those twenty minutes on the phone with you, I escaped. I wasn't in a hospital with my dad, uncertain of everything. I was in our world. I love our world.

But if I'm truly being honest, talking to you on the phone is kind of like watching a baseball game on TV instead of being at the game in the stadium with the players. It's simply not the same.

When I get home and finally see you again, I may not let you out of my sight for days. I miss you that much. Everything about you. I need to be in your space. I need to breath your air.

Part 16

JULY 27TH

So much has happened since the last diary entry. I had to go back and remind myself where we were then. I've been back home to see you only once. I'm sorry for that. I miss you.

Dad finally came home after a week in the hospital and a week in the rehabilitation facility. I'm with him 24/7. Two home health-care nurses come every day. It's hard watching him struggle to do the most simple things. I'm the adult now, and he's the child. The nurses say he's making progress, but I can't really tell. He sleeps most of the time. When he's awake, I'm only focused on him.

I've tried to straighten up his house, open the windows, make it look like someone lives here. I've found out things that have really surprised me. He had a girlfriend. Who knew? She gave him cute little cards and told him how special he was to her. I have no idea who she is though. She never signed the cards or put her name on them. I don't feel comfortable asking him about her. I assume that if they're still close, she'd come over, or call, or something. He'd never mentioned her to me. But that's my fault, I guess. I haven't talked to him on the phone in months. I haven't been to see him in over a year. I deeply regret that. Dad might not ever be the same. I should have made more of an effort.

I found an envelope of old pictures of me in a drawer in his bedroom. There were also old newspaper clippings of me and Father's Day cards I had given him. What should have brought me comfort also filled me with emptiness as I looked through my relationship with my dad, our memories, packed away in a drawer. It's strange how both emotions can exist simultaneously.

I was a happy kid who had a great childhood, but you wouldn't know it by looking at some of the pictures. I look like one of those people out of the 1800s who solemnly stares at the camera without the vaguest hint of a smile. It's kind of funny that looking at old pictures of me not smiling makes me smile. I want to tell that little boy in the pictures to lighten up, to smile, because someday he's going to meet you.

I miss you. This house is lonely. I'm lonely too. It's just me and my dad all day, every day. I miss you and I also miss sharing things with you. Dad and I watch a lot of really bad TV when he's awake, and I wish you were here to suffer through those terrible midday pharmaceutical television commercials with us. I think I know every side effect to every new prescription drug on the market. I have those depressing disclaimers memorized. If you were here, we'd find a way to make it fun. We could smile and laugh and make lemonade out of pharmaceutical commercials. Our phone calls every night are great, but I want to touch you, be in the same room with you. And again, the simultaneous emotion thing occurs every time we talk. I'm comforted by talking to you, but lonely and frustrated because we are not together.

I'm not sure how much longer I'll be here. Dad needs me and I need to be here. I'm learning a lot about being a good son and a caregiver, and also a lot about myself. I have a lot of time to think and plan out my future. When my mind goes there, to the future, you're always in it.

My boss and coworkers have been understanding. They've given me time off and let me work from here, but someday I want to go out on my own. I could freelance or start my own company and hire a few people. Or I could go out on my own and work with other freelancers. Maybe someday we could work together. Who knows? You're intelligent. I like creating things with you. I like being with you. We make a great team.

What I do know is that my immediate future is uncertain because Dad needs me. But my long-term future is not uncertain, because of you. And some days, that's what gets me through. Thinking about the future. Our future.

Part 17

AUGUST 23RD

I hope I can say here what I struggled to say to you in person. I knew what I wanted to say—the words, the delivery, the message. But when I was with you, I got frazzled. You do that to me. You have this way of taking my intentions and making them something else. And up until now, it has always been something better. But now, even though my intentions are pure, I've hurt you. I never wanted to hurt you. Ever. I tell myself that hurting you now is better than hurting you later. That's how I justify all of this in my mind. And I have to find a way to justify it ,because hurting you hurts me to the core.

I had my speech ready for you. I don't know why I picked a restaurant to tell you everything. It was a stupid move on my part. I was probably trying to take the emotion and vulnerability out of it because in a restaurant we had to be stoic. We couldn't be real. We had to be two people at a restaurant eating their dinner and having a difficult conversation. It was cowardly of me, I know. But I also know the power you have over me. How, when I look in your eyes, what once made perfect sense to me doesn't make sense at all. And what I thought I wasn't capable of understanding, makes perfect sense. You taught me how to love. You taught me how to let my guard down and let you in. Tonight, I couldn't let my guard down. I had to be strong. Strong for you, and for me too. You will probably never read this, but for my own sanity, I need to explain why I let go of one of the best things that has ever happened to me.

Dad isn't getting better, but he isn't really getting worse either. We've found our routine. It's the same every day, and I've accepted that this is my life now. I've finally realized that the more I resist this, the harder it will be. It'll be my life until the day he dies. I don't let myself question being his caregiver. Some things in life you should just do. Because if you question them, you might find loopholes. And I know what I'm doing is the right thing to do. I will not question that. I don't want to find a way out.

Tonight, when we were talking, I called you a distraction. That was a bad word choice. I didn't mean it like it sounded. Honestly, you have always been a distraction, or diversion, or escape, or whatever word I can't seem to find. I mean that in a positive way. You're what I think about when I want to think about something good. Your smile, your voice, your laugh. The way you make me feel. Your soft touch, your intellect, your creativity. You. Everything about you. It's what I think about. And when you are hundreds of miles away and I am here, I don't need to be thinking about you. I need to be thinking about Dad and how to make his life the best that it can be. I need to be thinking about work, especially since they are letting me work remotely. I need to be even better than I was when I was in the office every day. I have to prove myself and my worth to the company with every project. I don't have time for love. Happy diversions. Distractions. When Dad is awake, I must attend to his well-being. When he sleeps, I focus on my job. I have little time to focus on anything else. This rationale is not a cop-out, it's not an excuse to walk away from you. It is what it is. This is the life I now live.

And yes, we can continue like this, but that's not fair to you. You deserve the best. You deserve me for more than thirty minutes a day on the phone. You deserve a partner who is really a partner, someone who can walk through life with you step by step. And no, I would never ask you to move here, to sacrifice your life for my responsibilities. You deserve better, more. Let me write this down and express myself clearly. Whether you are in my life or not, you deserve the absolute best that life has to offer. You are the most amazing person I have ever met. You still take my breath away when you walk into a room. I feel this deep sense of connection every single time I touch you. But I don't want you to ever settle for less than you deserve. You only live once. This is not a practice round. You deserve better than what I can give you. As much as I cringe at the thought of you spending your life with someone else, my motives are pure. I want you to be happy, loved, and the number-one priority in someone's life. Your happiness is much more important than my selfish needs.

I'm sorry for the words I said. I'm sorry it has to end like this. I love you. I always will. You will always be a distraction when I think about you, because of all the feelings that come with thinking about you. And I mean that in a good way. Years from now, when I'm old and my world is much different than it is now, when I think of you, you'll still be a distraction. A wonderful, beautiful, happy distraction.

Part 18

SEPTEMBER 8TH

I really don't know why I am writing this. "My Story of Us" is now "My Diary of Me." Maybe writing this, putting my emotions down on paper, will help me adjust to life without you. I miss you terribly. I see things and think things, and I want to share them with you. I miss hearing about your day. I miss your voice. I pick up my phone to call you at least once a day, but I don't. I know that if I hear you, talk to you, I might lose my purpose here with my dad.

Do you remember the message you left me a few months ago? The one where you told me you were craving our favorite restaurant. Then you laughed and rambled until the phone just cut off. I listen to it when I'm at my lowest, missing you the most. It somehow gives me comfort. Sometimes I listen to it before I go to sleep at night hoping that I'll dream about you.

I'm not really in a good place right now. Work is much harder with me not being there. I can feel my closeness slipping away. Yesterday the team was all together in a meeting and I was Skyping with them. They were laughing and joking about something that happened at the office earlier that day and I was totally clueless, out of the loop. I felt invisible. I used to be the guy laughing the most and making others laugh.

But now I just sit and listen, lost to it all. They're nice and ask me about my day and my dad. But do they really want to know how we spend our days? How I feed him and help him stand up and use the bathroom? No one really wants to know the details. They're just asking because we have nothing else in common anymore. They're just being polite.

Now when Dad sleeps, I sleep too. I do my best to stay positive and encourage him. But nothing is changing. If anything, he's worse. It's incredibly difficult to watch someone you love wither away right in front of your eyes while you're completely helpless to make a difference. I can make sure he's fed and clean and gets his sleep and his meds. But I can't help him. The doctors and the nurses and the physical therapists can't help him. His quality of life is gone. He's locked in this house, locked in his body, with no escape. So, I sleep when he sleeps. That's our escape from these four walls.

Talking to you was the sunshine of my day. And I pushed you away. Now I have trouble finding the bright spots. It's dark here. Really dark. I don't question my decision, but I also don't know. That makes no sense. *This* makes no sense. The only thing I know is that I miss you. You made me a better person. And without you in my life, I seem to be going in the other direction.

My sunshine is gone.

Part 19

SEPTEMBER 22ND

I still think about you all the time. I wonder what you're doing and if you ever think about me. I imagine this other world where we're still together and I see you every day. We grow closer together in every way possible, intertwining our lives into a beautiful story. But that's only my imagination. I'm here. You're there, moving forward with your life.

The simple things we did together are what I miss the most. The conversations. Holding your hand. Snuggling with you on the couch and watching TV. Sitting across from you in a restaurant and feeling like the only two people in the universe.

I miss you terribly. I pick up the phone to call you daily. I just want to hear your voice. Hear about your day. Talk to you.

But I don't call you. You deserve more than what we would have long-distance. It's best for us not to talk. I know I would hang up the phone and feel empty or want to drive all night long just to see you. You might be able to handle a long-distance relationship, but I don't think I could. Not with you. I love you too much.

Did I tell you I miss you terribly? Did I tell you that "My Story of Us" was not supposed to have chapters like this? It was supposed to always go in a direction that brought us closer. It was supposed to have a happy ending. Did I tell you that this doesn't make sense to me? That there is an emptiness in me that aches for you all the time? I still miss you. I still love you. And I know in my heart I always will.

Part 20

OCTOBER 11TH

Today, I leaned on you. And you let me. You were the first person I called. It was instinct. I called you because I needed you. Our connection is too deep for me to suppress. Our connection is more than seeing each other or talking to each other every day. Our connection is layered, and I now know that the deepest of those layers is still a mystery to me. It's why I called you first. Because somehow, I knew I could.

Dad went into the hospital last night. He passed away this morning. My time on this earth together with my father is now over. I think I made peace with him. I think I understand him better, even though alcoholism can't really be understood. I have forgiven him for choosing his weakness over everything else in his life. If anything, I feel deep sadness and regret for him. He could have done so much more. He barely scraped the surface of life because his weakness was in control.

I met the woman who gave him the cards I told you about. She was his girlfriend. She came by one day unexpectedly to see him. When the doorbell rang, I assumed it was another home healthcare nurse or physical therapist. When I opened the door, she called me by name and gave me a hug. I didn't know this woman, but she knew me, knew everything about me. Dad had told her. He told her about my childhood and teen years and college. Told her how much he loved me and how he was proud of me. Told her that I was the best thing he did here on this earth. Told her that a man should leave at least one thing of significance behind to make the world a better place after he left it. He told her the one thing he had left behind that would make his life worthwhile on earth was me.

She also told me about my dad, how much she loved him. She said he could be the sweetest and most amazing person when he wasn't drinking, or "drinking a lot," she said, because he always drank. And, like so many others, she tried to save him. She tried to give him enough love for him to overcome his weakness and love her in return. I asked her if he pushed her away. She said she was the one who ended it because she couldn't watch him disappear each day. We bonded because even though I loved him and never gave up on him, I also avoided him because it hurt too much. I realized that in the last few months as I watched him disappear each day, I was forced to face what I had avoided for years.

My dad is at peace now. I fully believe that. His weakness is gone. He was loved by many, but he did not know how to love. Love is supposed to be a priority. Love is a wonderful feeling that you do not escape. My dad's love was stifled by his weakness. Dad's last love said she had been with him for two years before she had to walk away. She tried to save him for two years. That's a long time. I understand why she gave up.

She also said she saw him in me. I told her those words scared me to the core. She clarified that she saw the good in him in me. And that's also what he saw in me. He saw the good in him in me. The potential. The hope. The life without the weakness. The man who was able to love and not push love away. But she was wrong about that. I pushed you away. I took the best thing that has ever happened to me and let it go.

I pushed you away.

If my dad is right, and I'm the best thing that he left behind, then I'd better get to work on some things. The first thing I have to take care of is you. I let you go when I should have been pulling you closer. I needed you. You were right there when I needed you most.

I'm sorry. I told you I was sorry on the phone today, but those two words can't adequately express how deeply I feel them. So I'm going to show you. I'm not going to live the life my dad lived. I want to accept love and give it back. Make it my priority. I want to be loved by you and love you just as much in return.

Part 21

OCTOBER 17TH

Today, I laid it all out to you. I told you how I really feel. I let my guard down and let you inside. I spoke from my heart and not my head. It's kind of funny that talking to you from my heart was one of the most logical things I've ever done—telling you how I feel about you with unfiltered and unguarded truth.

I was tired from the funeral. I was tired from seeing family and friends and my dad's friends I'd never met. I was tired of the stories. I was tired from making tough decisions about a funeral and an estate and picking out the clothes he would be buried in. I was tired of being stoic. I was emotionally and physically wrung out, not a single drop of energy left in my tired body. I wanted to lie down in a dark room and sleep, to hibernate until life came back into me.

Then you walked through the door. I felt my world shift. I felt relief and comfort just seeing you. Just knowing I was in your presence. You are my rock. No, you are my mountain. And as much as I tried to shut you out, to pretend that my life could go in a direction without you, you were always there with me. Mountains don't disappear. They don't go away just because of circumstance. What was I thinking, pushing you away when I needed you the most?

Later, when we were alone, I cried on your shoulder. I told you I loved you and that I wanted to be with you always. During good times and bad. I told you I never wanted to spend another day without hearing your voice or seeing your face. And that these past months without you were excruciating.

I told you that if you felt the same way, I would do whatever was necessary to win your heart back. And that I would never, ever close the door to us again. I would never take you for granted. I would love you without boundaries and limitations. That I was yours, if you would be mine.

Then you said yes, I was yours, and you were mine. I have no words for how I felt in that moment. A weight lifted from my body. I was surprised you let me back into your life that quickly. Relieved. Grateful. I let us down when I pushed you away. And I promise you, it will never happen again. You, we, will always be my priority.

I love you. And I will always be there for you. Let's do this. Let's keep writing the Story of Us. Together.

Part 20

OCTOBER 25TH

I am amazed at how quickly we fell back into being us. It's like there never was time apart. Like I never pushed you away. But it's also different. I think I love you even more. I appreciate you more. I notice more now. All the wonderful things that make you, you.

When I was in high school, I tore my ACL playing basketball and had to have surgery. I learned a lot about myself then. I learned I had taken almost everything for granted and the little things that meant the most had been unnoticed by me. I learned the importance of being able to tie my own shoe, bend my knee, walk without a limp, sleep on my side, get in and out of a car. At seventeen, I'd felt invincible, like I had the world in the palm of my hand. But as I was recovering from surgery, I realized that the world had me in the palm of *its* hand. It humbled me. I ended up having three surgeries on that knee in eighteen months. And you know what? It changed me, made me a better person. I began to appreciate the simple things. I began opening doors when I saw someone on crutches or an older person who was struggling to walk. I learned about empathy. I learned that the human body was incredibly strong, yet incredibly fragile. I don't think, at seventeen, I could have understood any of that if not for the knee surgeries. I had to experience it firsthand to learn the many things life needed to teach me.

And with you, I feel the same way. I loved you. I loved everything about you. But while we were apart, I began to love and appreciate you even more. Your absence from my life created a void I can't even describe. At first, I tried not to think of you, to block you out. But that was impossible. Then I would relive moments we had shared in my mind. Recreate the sound of your voice, the smell of your hair, the comfort of your hand in my hand. I told myself the memory of you was better than the real you. But I was wrong. That was a lie. And now that we're together again, it is the same, but it is also different. Better.

I was lost without you. I'm not a dependent person. I don't need someone to cater to me or give me attention. I'm self-sufficient. I can survive on my own. But when I'm with you, life is better. The world makes more sense, or maybe the things in the world that don't make sense simply don't matter anymore. Being apart from you made me realize how much I need you in my life. In this world, some things need other things to thrive. Humans need oxygen, water, food, and shelter. These things allow us to survive.

But humans also need love. Love allows us to thrive, to become better. I know now that I need your love. I need you.

Part 21

NOVEMBER 3RD

The definition of darkness is "the absence or partial absence of light." Without darkness, it is difficult to know light. With light, it is impossible to understand the true meaning of darkness. This makes sense to me now more than ever. My life without you was much different from my life with you. And knowing what we had, then didn't have, so clearly emphasized the significance of us to me. Now I better understand it. The smallest details bring me peace. We have found our way again. Thank you for sliding back into my life as if I'd never pushed you away. It further proves that it is meant to be. Everything is familiar, yet new. Crisper. I love you even more than I'd ever thought possible.

Tonight was simple. We bought food. We cooked. We ate. We spent time together. Tonight was also beautifully tangled. And trust me, I like being entangled with you. Please don't laugh. I can't believe I'm admitting this to you, but there was a moment at the store when we were getting food that took my breath away. You were standing in front of the fruit. The mist came out to spray the produce with water, and you jumped a little and pulled your hand back and laughed. You were so beautiful in that moment. So pure. Just being you. You were relieved and embarrassed and laughing. I loved seeing you in that moment, looking into my eyes and sharing it with me.

Later, we were preparing dinner together back at my place in my little kitchen. You were at the sink and the water was running. Even though I couldn't see your face, I loved that moment too. Seeing your hands under the water, your focus and posture on the task at hand. Hearing your voice as you told me about your best friend in high school. I was imagining you back then while simultaneously seeing you now. I got lost in that moment, too. Your perfection took hold of me. I wanted to come up behind you and pull you against me. But instead, I just stood and looked at you. I tried to capture every detail.

And when we were at the table eating our delicious creation, there was a moment then, when you pulled the glass up to your mouth and hesitated while you listened to me tell you about my best friend in high school. Your lips were touching the glass, and you just held them there, slightly hesitating before you took a drink. That moment stirred me. Made me realize I'm a man. You made me stumble over my words and lose my train of thought. I wanted to tell you what you had just done to me. I wanted to take your hand and take you someplace else. But instead, I gathered my composure and finished my sentence, focusing on dinner and our wonderful conversation.

Then, after dinner, there were many moments I won't fully describe here. Those moments should only be known to us. Moments when you make me feel like a man, an *inamorato* who is purposeful and gallant. In those moments, I am a person deeply and contentedly entangled with you.

Most of the time my life is like a movie, twenty-four frames per second or whatever the standard is. Sometimes, if I'm fully immersed in an activity, the world goes into slow motion, and I can see things more clearly. But with you, sometimes there are moments when the world comes to a complete stop. Like a painting or a photograph, these moments are captured in my mind. And with these moments comes the entanglement. You become imbedded into the deepest layers of my consciousness, and we slowly become intertwined.

Part 22

DECEMBER 16TH

Somewhere in this story I mentioned that my mind works better when I collaborate with you. I know you feel the same because together we came up with a wonderful idea. Today was one of the most memorable days of my life. When we came up with the idea, I never imagined it would have the impact on me that it did.

Our initial conversation was about holidays and how they stressed me out, especially Christmas and Thanksgiving. When I was growing up, after Mom and Dad divorced, I always felt like I needed to be in two or three places at once. I always had to choose. When you add stepparents to the mix and step-grandparents, it can get complicated. When you're a child, you have no choice where you spend your holidays. You just go, shuffled around like luggage in an airport. I remember going to three different houses on Christmas Eve. I once ate Thanksgiving dinner four times in one day. As I got older, I felt a little guilty for complaining about having too much family in my life because I knew some people didn't have any. As an adult, nothing had changed. The holidays continued to stress me out.

Our idea was to give. I received a Christmas bonus this year I truly didn't expect. We took the money from the bonus and gave it to others.

We went to the stores, but we didn't shop. We watched others shop, and we gave. It was a humbling experience. It made me realize that Christmas has gotten a little lost somewhere, that we tend to focus on things and not people. We watched shoppers rush and stress over toys and clothes and candles and all sorts of stuff. In the end, it's just junk that really doesn't matter. Watching people of all shapes and sizes, ages, and backgrounds was fascinating. Like me, everyone seemed a little stressed by Christmas. There were a few smiles, but there were many more furrowed brows.

So we followed our plan. We went to stores and bought gift cards. Then we gave those gift cards to people shopping in those stores. Some people thought we were pranking them. But I think it was your genuine smile that convinced them otherwise. When people asked why, we told them the money we were going to spend on each other was better used going to others. We told them we already had everything we could possibly need. We had each other.

One lady cried. Some seem confused. One man simply refused and told us he only dressed like he didn't have money. That made me laugh, and I'm still not sure if he was telling the truth. We asked those who didn't want to accept the card to please give the gift to someone else. One man said, "Here," and immediately gave it back to us. That was also funny. We gave five gift cards to one family in a clothing store. One kid at a toy store told his mother we must work for Santa. An older gentleman took the card on the condition that we would help him pick out a gift for his wife. That was also fun. We ate lunch with him, and he paid for the meal so we bought the meal for the people at the table next to us. (That was his idea.)

As I write this, I realize what we did today was in no way earth-shattering. No person we gave a gift card to was down on their luck or down to their last dime. They were all just people trying to get through the holidays, trying to find that perfect gift. What I learned today is that spending time with people and giving them a little part of yourself is the real gift. It is much easier to give someone something you buy in a store, that was made by someone else, than to give a person a little part of yourself. I hope we can always remember this.

After I finish writing this, I'll go to bed and sleep with a peace I haven't known for a while. Holidays make more sense to me. Somewhere through the years I'd gotten lost in Christmas. Right now, if I could have one gift for Christmas, it would be to have dinner with my father one more time. It definitely would not be a car or a shirt or a candle. I now realize that when I stressed about what to buy my dad every year, I should have given him a gift that would have been perfect for both of us. I should have just spent time with him.

Part 23

DECEMBER 25TH

In the past week, we've spent more time together than since the day we met. And I can't imagine my life without you. We were meant to be. This becomes clearer to me every day. The more time I spend with you, the more time I want to spend with you. I believe the holidays are a time of reflection. The world slows down and makes you think. It reunites you with family and friends and those who have had an impact in your life.

I can still feel all the Christmas mornings I've ever lived. I feel the excitement of opening presents as a little boy. I see myself helping Mom pick up the wrapping paper from the floor. I can smell the popcorn popping as we prepared the homemade Christmas strings for the tree. I can taste Christmas dinner at my grandmother's house and hear the laughter at the table. It's all there, vivid and still incredibly real. As I've gotten older, I realize life is about change. The Christmases in my memory are much different than they are now, but still deeply connected to my past. We all have these memories buried within us. Christmas has a way of dusting off the picture frames and showing us the captured moments that are solidified in our minds. If we're lucky, those moments are spent with those we love.

This year, I spent Christmas with you. It was wonderful. The ache of missing those who are no longer in my life became something different. It became a gratefulness, knowing I was once lucky enough to spend Christmas with them. I realized those memories are real and still alive within me. And so are the loved ones. Spending Christmas with you gave me a new insight about memories. This year, we made new ones together and the place in my soul where I store memories is becoming filled with you. There is nothing better than making memories with someone you deeply love. Those memories will always be there. It's what makes us who we are.

I know my memories are in the past. But I also know the memories that await me are in the future. They are sitting out there waiting for me to grab them, hold them in my hand, and let them unfold. If we, as humans, have any control over future memories, I want to make my memories with you. This year's Christmas memories were wonderful. Thank you for those. Thank you for inviting me into your world. It was the best gift you could have given me.

Merry Christmas.

Part 24

DECEMBER 31ST/JANUARY 1ST

I am writing this January 1, but it's not only about today, it's also about yesterday and every day for the rest of my life. I went back and read the first entry in this diary, the Story of Us, written on January 1, one year ago today. I had three resolutions. I wanted to be a better me, turn down my earbuds, and win your heart. What a year it has been. I did okay with the earbud volume. I also realized that some songs just need to be turned up! I indeed won your heart, but ultimately, you won mine. The more I got to know the real you, the more I liked you, the more I loved you. And the part about being a better me? Well, I accomplished that, also because of you. You taught me how to love, how to look at my own life and realize where my priorities should be. I've still got a long way to go. Yes, I am indeed a work in progress, and I will be until the day I leave this earth. But I want to be a better me with each passing day—for me, for you, for us.

We spent the entire last day of the year together. We had breakfast, were lazy, watched television, snuggled on the couch, laughed, talked, napped, and simply loved each other. I could not have asked for a better day. Our night was spent at the museum, a New Year's Eve scavenger hunt called "Auld Lang Find." Our job was to find things in the museum that were about the passing year. We dressed up, and you looked beautiful. And though I'm constantly telling you how stunning you are, please know I adore your mind just as much, if not more. This became all too obvious to me as we made our way through the museum, and you meticulously and flawlessly deciphered messages and uncovered clues way beyond my pay grade. So, you are beautiful and intelligent and I am the luckiest man in the world.

The scavenger hunt finale took place in the planetarium. Even though other people, other scavenger-hunt hunters, also had access to the planetarium, I still consider it our room. It's where we spent Valentine's Day having a picnic under the stars. That seems like such a long time ago, but my memory of that night is still so incredibly vivid. Your face when you saw I had a key to the museum was priceless. I hope I can continue to give you happy surprises and see that face for the rest of my life.

I got to see that facial expression again tonight. The planetarium might have been the scavenger hunt finale for everyone else, but it wasn't for us. One more clue remained. One more "find" awaited you. You solved the clue that led you to the elevator that led you to the observatory that led you to the telescope. When you looked through the telescope to find the clue in the stars, you saw a four-word question inside the lens. You discovered the most significant, life-changing four words I have ever strung together. "Will You Marry Me?" When you realized this clue was just for you and really had nothing at all to do with the scavenger hunt, you spun around and found me on one knee to say those four words as I looked into your eyes.

For historical purposes, which is appropriate because we were making history in a museum, you said "yes" before the question left my mouth. (And for the record, I want to thank the museum crew for figuring out how to put my words in a telescope lens.)

As I put the ring on your finger, emotion got the best of me and I was left speechless. Sometimes in life, words can't adequately express emotion, and the moment becomes much bigger than us. Even as I write this now, words can't describe that experience.

Thank you for a wonderful night. Thank you for a wonderful year. Thank you for letting me into your world and letting me love you. I can't wait for our lives to unfold together. There's a term in science called quantum entanglement. It is a physical phenomenon that describes when pairs of particles move into a quantum state. When this happens, each particle can no longer be described independently from the other, even when the particles are separated by a large distance. To a scientist, this is science. To me, this is also love. This is how I see us, quantumly entangled. No matter where you are, or what you are doing, I will be there with you. And you are always with me.

I can't wait to show you "My Story of Us," the story of the last year, our first year. I hope years from now, decades, we can look back and relive the beginning of something that became more wonderful than our imaginations even allowed us to dream about.

Happy New Year. I love you.

About the Author

Chris Brinkley is an experienced narrator, voice-over artist, NCAA Division I broadcaster, radio personality, and emcee. He is known as the voice of Penny Reid's Winston Brothers Series, narrating and voicing all six brothers in the popular audiobook collection. Brinkley also narrates Reid's Handcrafted Mystery Series and the Smartypants Romance Green Valley Chronicles. He is currently one of the top storytellers heard on Kevin Costner's HearHere travel app and is heard weekly on the Curio audio journalism app. He is heard regularly on several documentary series on the History Channel, including D-Day in HD, and also on PBS. He co-produced, wrote, and hosted two nationally syndicated radio shows heard on stations throughout the US.

Find Chris Brinkley online:
Website:http://chrisbrinkleyproductions.com/
Facebook: https://www.facebook.com/chrisbrinkleyproductions

Find Smartypants Romance online:
Website: www.smartypantsromance.com
Facebook: www.facebook.com/smartypantsromance/
Goodreads: www.goodreads.com/smartypantsromance
Twitter: @smartypantsrom
Instagram: @smartypantsromance
Newsletter: https://smartypantsromance.com/newsletter/

Also by Smartypants Romance

Green Valley Chronicles

The Love at First Sight Series

Baking Me Crazy by Karla Sorensen (#1)

Batter of Wits by Karla Sorensen (#2)

Steal My Magnolia by Karla Sorensen(#3)

Fighting For Love Series

Stud Muffin by Jiffy Kate (#1)

Beef Cake by Jiffy Kate (#2)

Eye Candy by Jiffy Kate (#3)

The Donner Bakery Series

No Whisk, No Reward by Ellie Kay (#1)

The Green Valley Library Series

Love in Due Time by L.B. Dunbar (#1)

Crime and Periodicals by Nora Everly (#2)

Prose Before Bros by Cathy Yardley (#3)

Shelf Awareness by Katie Ashley (#4)

Carpentry and Cocktails by Nora Everly (#5)

Love in Deed by L.B. Dunbar (#6)

Dewey Belong Together by Ann Whynot (#7)

Scorned Women's Society Series

My Bare Lady by Piper Sheldon (#1)

The Treble with Men by Piper Sheldon (#2)

The One That I Want by Piper Sheldon (#3)

Park Ranger Series

Happy Trail by Daisy Prescott (#1)

Stranger Ranger by Daisy Prescott (#2)

The Leffersbee Series

Been There Done That by Hope Ellis (#1)

The Higher Learning Series

Upsy Daisy by Chelsie Edwards (#1)

Seduction in the City

Cipher Security Series

Code of Conduct by April White (#1)

Code of Honor by April White (#2)

Cipher Office Series

Weight Expectations by M.E. Carter (#1)

Sticking to the Script by Stella Weaver (#2)

Cutie and the Beast by M.E. Carter (#3)

Weights of Wrath by M.E. Carter (#4)

Common Threads Series

Mad About Ewe by Susannah Nix (#1)

Give Love a Chai by Nanxi Wen (#2)

Educated Romance

Work For It Series

Street Smart by Aly Stiles (#1)

Heart Smart by Emma Lee Jayne (#2)

Lessons Learned Series

Under Pressure by Allie Winters (#1)

Made in the USA
Coppell, TX
18 October 2021